HEATHCLIFF SPINS A YARN

The funniest feline in America delights millions of fans every day as he appears in over 500 newspapers. You'll have a laugh a minute as Heathcliff tangles with the milkman, the fish store owner, the tuna fisherman and just about everyone else he runs into. If you're looking for some fun, look no further, Heathcliff is here.

HEATHCLIFF SPINS A YARN

ISBN: 0-448-12619-2
A Tempo Books Original
Tempo Books is registered in the U.S. Patent Office
Published simultaneously in Canada
Printed in the United States of America

HEATHCLIFF
SPINS A YARN

by

Geo Gately

tempo
books
GROSSET & DUNLAP
A Filmways Company
Publishers • New York

"OH, OH!... THERE'S GOING TO BE TROUBLE AT THE FISH MARKET!"

"HEATHCLIFF!"

"HE'S BEEN HANGING AROUND WITH A PRETTY TOUGH CROWD!"

6-8
© 1977
McNaught Synd., Inc.
WHACK!

"EXPLAIN TO HIM THAT TALENT WILL NOT BE A FACTOR."

"HE'S ADDED WOOFERS AND TWEETERS!"

"WE CAN DO WITHOUT AN UMPIRE!"

"GOING TO TRY A LITTLE DIPLOMACY ?!"

6-14
STAGE
DOOR
© 1977
McNaught Synd., Inc.
STAGE
DOOR

"HELP!!"

"7¢ OFF ON WHOOPEE CAT FOOD!"

"YOU'LL HAVE TO OPEN WIDER THAN THAT!"

"HEATHCLIFF'S TV FAVORITE IS FONZIE!"

"NOT AGAIN!"

"HE WON THE CRUISE IN A CAT FOOD CONTEST!"

© 1977 McNaught Synd., Inc.
6-22

"NO YOU DON'T, HEATHCLIFF!... THERE'LL BE NONE OF YOUR BOTTLE BREAKING TRICKS TODAY!"

6-24
THUD!
© 1977
McNaught Synd., Inc.
DANGER
FALLING
ROCK

"WOULD YOU MIND?!..."

6-28
© 1977
McNaught Synd., Inc.

"IF YOU DON'T MIND, I'LL GIVE THE INSTRUCTIONS!"

"HE'S PUTTING ON HIS OWN FIREWORKS DISPLAY!"

"YOU NEVER KNOW ***WHO*** WILL SHOW UP ON THESE PACKAGE TOURS!"

"HEATHCLIFF DIDN'T SEEM TO CARE FOR THAT NEW CAT FOOD."

"I GUESS NOT!"

"I DON'T LIKE MOBILES!"

"THAT REMINDS ME....DID YOU FEED HEATHCLIFF BEFORE WE LEFT?"

"MORE MICE ?!"

"YOU PROBABLY HURT IT SNEAKING OVER THE FENCE!"

"I THINK I HEAR FANG SCRATCHING TO COME IN."

"NOTHING FOR THE NUTMEGS TODAY."

"YOU'RE NOT GOING!.... AND THAT'S FINAL!!"

"HEATHCLIFF'S A PEST ON THE GOLF COURSE!"

"EVERY ONCE IN AWHILE, HE LIKES TO REVISIT HIS BIRTHPLACE."

7-14
© 1977 McNaught Synd., Inc.
"THERE'S A LONG DRIVE......IT'S GOING...IT'S GOING...
.....IT'S....."

"IF HE SHOWS AN INTEREST, THEN HE SHOULD BE ENCOURAGED!"

"OKAY...I'LL HAVE TO MEND THAT ALSO!"

"I CAN'T BELIEVE IT!...'PRETTY KITTY' FINISHED DEAD LAST!"

"NO!...YOU CAN'T BLOW THE SIREN!"

FLORIST
7-20
SAY IT WITH FLOWERS
© 1977 McNaught Synd., Inc.

"HERE WE SEE A MAJESTIC NATURAL WONDER!
... AND BEHIND HIM IS...."

"HE'D LIKE TO BORROW A CUP OF FISH."

"HEATHCLIFF NUTMEG?...HE JUST CHECKED OUT."

"THERE'S YOUR TROUBLE.... MICE IN THE CARBURETOR!"

7-26
© 1977
McNaught Synd., Inc.
FLAP

"THE GENTLEMAN WOULD LIKE TO BUY THE HOUSE A DRINK."

"OH, YOU ALWAYS CRITICIZE MY DRIVING!"

"IT'S NOT NECESSARY TO SUBMIT YOUR RESUMÉ!"

"IT'S AN ALBUM OF THIRTY OF HIS BIGGEST HITS!"

"I'M EXPECTING A MESSAGE BY CARRIER PIGEON!"

"DON'T STARTLE HIM!... HE'S SLEEPWALKING!"

8-3
© 1977 McNaught Synd., Inc.
BEWARE OF DOG

"WE ONCE SERVED TIME TOGETHER."

8-5
© 1977
McNaught Synd., Inc.
CATS BOARDED
"SORRY, MA'AM....NO VACANCY."
CATS BOARDED

"MY! WHAT A NICE, WARM GREETING!"

"HE ALWAYS CRIES AT FISH MARKET OPENINGS!"

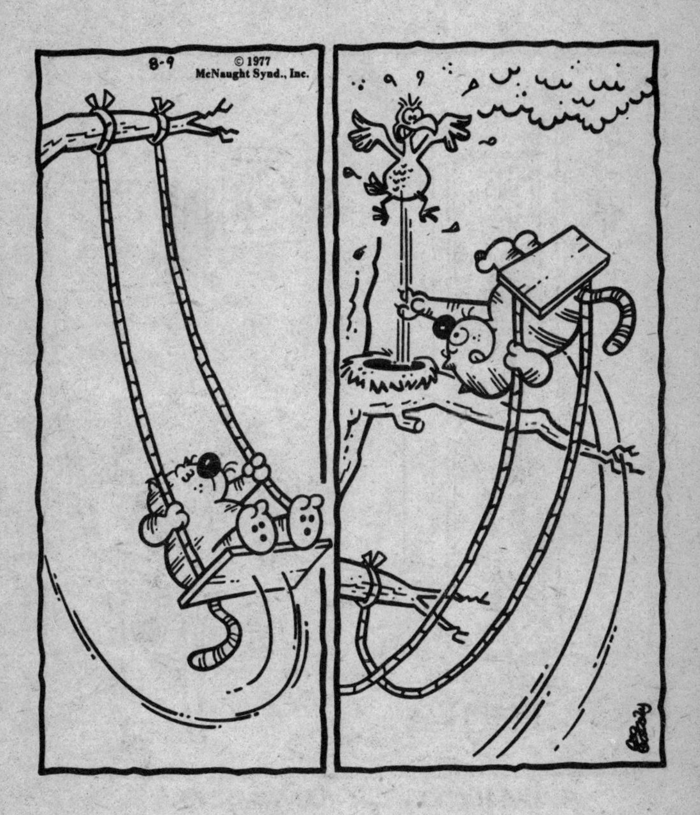
8-9
© 1977
McNaught Synd., Inc.

"SORRY TO KEEP YOU WAITING."

"I'M TELLING YOU... IT'S ***NOT*** HORSEMEAT!"

"WE'D CAPSIZE FOR SURE, IF IT WASN'T FOR HEATHCLIFF!"

"THAT'S SUPPOSED TO BE USED FOR GROOMING!"

1977
McNaught Synd., Inc.
8-15
VET

"SPIKE TANGLED WITH A SKUNK!"

"YOU'RE SPOILING HIM!"

"CHAUNCY WON A SPECIAL RIBBON FOR 'MOST LOVABLE'!"

"A DRUM ROLL!... SIGNIFYING AN EVENT IS ABOUT TO TAKE PLACE!"

"WE JUST WANTED YOU TO ***TASTE*** IT!!"

"LOOKING FOR A TV DINNER?"

8-23
1977 McNaught Synd., Inc.
HOGAN'S ALLEY
"HEATHCLIFF'S STOPPING BY TO VISIT ALL YOU TOUGH GUYS!"
HOGAN'S ALLEY

"HE'S IN HERE, REVIEWING HIS FIGHT FILMS!"

"I MUST COMPLIMENT YOU ON YOUR HUMOROUS SIGN OUT FRONT!"

"***WHAT*** HUMOROUS SIGN?!!"

"TODAY'S GUEST WILL NOW DEMONSTRATE WHAT A CAT CAN DO TO A FLOWER BED...."

"LORD HEATHCLIFF NUTMEG AND LADY SONJA JABLONSKI!"

"WE'D LIKE ANOTHER BOX OF EXPLODING BONES!"

"YOUR FIGHT SCHEDULE IS BOOKED SOLID THROUGH THURSDAY ...MAYBE YOU CAN SQUEEZE HIM IN ON FRIDAY."

8-31
© 1977
McNaught Synd., Inc.

"HE'D LIKE TO TAKE IT FOR A TEST DRIVE."

"HE HAS NO FRACTURE... THANKS TO AN EXTREMELY THICK SKULL!"

"IT'S FOURTEEN KARAT GOLD!"

"BE QUIET!...YOU WANTED TO COME ALONG!"

"I'D BETTER GO IN... I DON'T WANT TO BE LATE ON MY FIRST DAY BACK!"

9-7
© 1977
McNaught Synd., Inc.
"HERE COMES GREAT, BIG, LOVABLE CHAUNCY!"

"BLEEAH!...THIS CAT FOOD SMELLS AWFUL!...
...HEATHCLIFF WILL LOVE IT!"

9-9
© 1977
McNaught Synd., Inc.
TUNNEL
OF LOVE

"HE WANTS THEM ALL TO MEET THEIR GRANDFATHER!"

"THERE'S SOMEONE HERE LOOKING FOR YOUR FATHER."

9-13
40¢
RED HOT FRANKS
© 1977
McNaught Synd., Inc.

"CHAUNCY THINKS HE'S A LAP DOG."

"IT'S GOING TO TAKE MORE THAN EXERCISING WITH A HULA HOOP!"

"THAT'S NOT THE WAY WE DO THINGS HERE!"

"I'M TOO ALERT FOR YOU TO PULL ONE OF YOUR TRICKS THIS MORNING!"

"WHAT HAPPENED?!"

"HAVE YOU SEEN A FOX?"

9-21
© 1977
McNaught Synd., Inc.
"PARDON ME...IS THIS THE DOG AND CAT HOSPITAL?"
"NO...THIS IS THE HEATHCLIFF COMPLAINT CENTER!"

"AND PERHAPS MONSIEUR WOULD CARE FOR AN AFTER-DINNER LIQUEUR?"

"HE'S FEELING MUCH BETTER!"

9-24
© 1977
McNaught Synd., Inc.
BEWARE
OF
DOG
BEWARE
DOG
Geo Gately

"ACCORDING TO THIS, ONE OF THE SHIPS IN THE TUNA FLEET WENT DOWN."

9-27
© 1977
McNaught Synd., Inc.
PET
GROOMING
SALON
PET
GROOMING
SALON

"NOT MANY COUPLES SHOWED UP FOR THE HAYRIDE!"

"OH, DEAR!...SOMEONE IS A SORE LOSER!!"

"NOW, YOU WERE COMING UP THE WALK, DELIVERING THE MILK... AND THEN WHAT HAPPENED?"

"YOU CAN CHECK FOR CAT FOOD COUPONS WHEN I'VE FINISHED THE PAPER!"

KING
10-3
© 1977 McNaught Synd., Inc.

"GETTING ALL SET FOR THE WORLD SERIES OPENER?"

10-5
© 1977 McNaught Synd., Inc.

"THERE'S NOTHING WRONG WITH YOUR ARCH!"

"I THINK YOUR LIGHT IS DISTURBING HIM."

"TO MR. HEATHCLIFF NUTMEG...'DEAR SIR, I'M SORRY YOU DON'T FEEL PROPERLY REPRESENTED...!'"

10-10
© 1977
McNaught Synd., Inc.
COMPLAINT
DEPT.
CATNIP
SCRATCHING
POST

"YOU AGAIN?!"

"HE'S GOT AN ACCOMPLICE!"

"HE'S VERY TICKLISH!"

"I WISH YOU'D LEARN TO RING THE DOORBELL!"

"HE ENJOYS A FAMILY STYLE RESTAURANT."

"...AND HERE WE HAVE YOUR SIGNED CONFESSION!"

"HE'S GOT A VERY BUSY DAY, TOMORROW."

"HEATHCLIFF WOULDN'T PLAY DOLL CARRIAGE, SO I THOUGHT I'D MAKE HIM JEALOUS WITH CHAUNCY!"

10-19
"HE DUMPED THAT GARBAGE CAN AND NEVER TOUCHED ANY OF IT!"
© 1977 McNaught Synd., Inc.
"HMMPH!...THAT'S STRANGE!"

"YESIREE, FOLKS.... THREE OUT OF FOUR CATS PREFER 'LIVER LUMPS'!"

"MASCOTS DO NOT BLOCK FIELD GOALS!"

"OH, DEAR!... MY SLIP IS SHOWING!"

"KEEP OUR MASCOT AWAY FROM THE TACKLING DUMMY!"

"FINISHED WITH YOUR SCRATCHING POST, HONEYBUN?"

Elite
FISH
TUNA
"OUT!...OUT!!"
FLOUNDER
LOBSTER
"NOW YOU MADE ME DROP ALL MY SIGNS!"
10-26
© 1977 McNaught Synd., Inc.
Elite
FISH MARKET
CRAB
SALMON

"CATNIP AND ROSES."

"I'LL TELL THIS FISH STORY!"